SUPER SAVED BY THE BELL SCRAPBOOK

by Beth Goodman

SCHOLASTIC INC.
New York Toronto London Auckland Sydney

ISBN 0-590-47168-6

Book designed by Dawn Antoniello

12 11 10 9 8 7 6 5 4 3 2 1   3 4 5 6 7 8/9

Printed in U.S.A.   08

First Scholastic printing, April 1993

Hey there guys, how's it going? It's me, Zack Morris, in person (well, not really in person, but let's not get too technical). I'm here to tell you that the last couple of years I've spent at Bayside High in Palisades, California, have been the best years of my life! Who knew high school would turn out to be so much fun? Well, I guess with great friends like Screech, Kelly, Lisa, Jessie, and even Slater, Bayside had to be a blast.

Anyway, I was getting pretty nostalgic the other day thinking about graduation and all the great times my friends and I have had together. That's when I decided it would be fun (and a pretty cool gesture on my part) to put together a scrapbook sort of thing, you know, with lots of photos and stuff. There were *so* many good snapshots I dug up! My friends got a bunch together for me, too. It was really hard to decide which photos to include in the scrapbook. But, of course, I did my best and once again I pulled it off with flying colors! Turn the page and you'll see what I mean. Enjoy!

Guess who? It's me again. Don't I look great ?

My best friend and class clown, Screech.

This is Lisa. Her best friend is her father's credit card!

Slater and I are known to have our disagreements, but he's a pretty good guy ...
I guess.

Jessie is the one we all turn to if we want some sound advice.

Last, but certainly not least, is Kelly. She's the most beautiful girl at Bayside!

MOI, ZACK

I like school a lot, but school doesn't alway: like me. I do a much better job hanging o at the Max. The Max is by far the enti: gang's favorite hangout. This is me at th Max looking very cool!

Here's me close up! I want you to take a good look at my great smile. It's no wonder I'm the school hunk.

o, no, it's not Tom Cruise in *Risky Business*. only me dancing around at Screech's use when his parents weren't home. I nd out later that the girls were spying on and saw me dancing like a dork. How barrassing!

Don't Kelly and I make a beautiful couple? I remember the time we were married. Well, not *really* married. It was a school project our principal, Mr. Belding, came up with. We all had to pair up and *pretend* we were married. It went really well for me and Kelly — until we had to take Screech on as our teenage son. The arguing between us "parents" began right away. It turned out okay at the end when all the "husbands" took their "wives" out for a romantic dinner at the Max.

SCREECH

One thing about my good buddy Screech is that he's always there when I need him. There was the time I was selling friendship bracelets....I promised everyone who bought a bracelet that *a friend* was included with each purchase. Of course, that *friend* was Screech. He ended up being a slave to *everyone* who bought a bracelet.

This was the time I got Screech appointed hall monitor. Screech let the job go to his head a bit. He got so into it, he told me he had a fantasy that he was RoboScreech of the halls! Well, no one ever said that Screech wasn't a little weird!

See what I mean? Screech is *weird!*

Homework:
1. English - Read
   PP 20-42
2. Science - Read
   chapter two
3. Math - complete
   exercise #

LISA

Lisa is really into clothing. She's the school fashion plate. This is just one of her several *hundred* outfits.

One time Lisa got into big trouble when she went on a buying spree with her dad's credit card. She ended up spending a few hundred dollars — and she had only four days to come up with the cash before the credit card bill came in! Lisa was desperate to earn the money. She tried everything she could think of. Selling kisses to nerds, auctioning off her clothing, and waitressing at the Max were just a few of the things she stooped to. Come to think of it, it was kind of funny seeing Lisa actually *work*. Eventually she and her father came to a mutual agreement, and it all turned out okay.

Here's Lisa sporting another one of her trendy outfits!

SLATER

I have to admit, when Slater first moved to town a few years ago, he got on my nerves. We were always arguing over Kelly. We both liked her a lot. It took some time, but eventually Slater realized that Jessie was a better match for him. That worked out for me just fine!

Slater may come across as a tough guy because he loves wrestling *and* he has the muscles to prove it! But when it comes down to it, I think he's a softy.

■ feel like such a jerk every time I think of the time Slater went away with his family for a few days. He asked me to take care of his best friend, Artie. Artie was a chameleon who traveled all over the world with Slater before his family settled down in California. Anyway, Artie died while I was chameleon-sitting. Slater pretended not to care, but I knew he did. The whole gang held a funeral for Artie. I think that made Slater feel a little better.

Jessie's a great kid. She is usually too serious for her own good, though. You know, Jessie's into all sorts of causes like women's rights, environmental stuff, and social issues. Whew! Just thinking about all that makes me tired!

Who would have ever thought these two would make a great couple? From the second Jessie and Slater met, they argued. They still argue, but now I guess when they make up, it's a lot more fun!

I remember one time when Jessie needed her friends to be the level-headed ones. She was really stressing over this geometry midterm. Jessie is always putting pressure on herself to do well, but this time she went way overboard. I found out that Jessie was taking caffeine pills to keep herself awake so she could pack in the studying. We finally convinced her that they were bad for her. And she appreciated our help.

KE LY

Kelly, Kelly, Kelly ... what can I say about Kelly? Doesn't she look great in this photo I took of her in the park a while back? We were dating at the time. Now we're just good friends.

We made a great couple, and we had loads of fun together. It killed me when she told me she wanted to break up with me. For days I didn't want to leave my house because I was afraid I might see her. After a while I knew I would be okay, and I'd find someone else to date—I mean, who wouldn't want to go out with a hunk like myself?

Aahhh, a vision of beauty ... oh, and Kelly looks pretty good here, too!

MR BELDING

This is Mr. Belding, our principal. He's a pretty good guy and a pretty good principal. What I like about him is — it's so easy to take advantage of him!

He's not always willing to admit it, but I know we're his favorite students. I personally drive him more crazy than any other student at Bayside. It's a fact that I spend a lot more time in his office than anyone else. I think he holds a special place in his heart for me — a *very special* place!

THE GIRLS!

The school cafeteria is our only escape from the classrooms during the day. It's also a meeting ground for those who love to gossip. Here are Kelly and Jessie wrapped up in some serious gossiping.

The fashion queens! I'm so glad I had my camera with me in school that day. I think I'll tell Lisa that her earrings totally clash with the rest of her outfit in this picture. Hey, what are friends for?

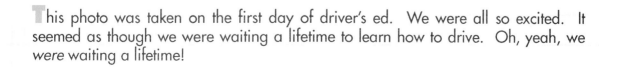

This photo was taken on the first day of driver's ed. We were all so excited. It seemed as though we were waiting a lifetime to learn how to drive. Oh, yeah, we *were* waiting a lifetime!

MEMORIES

Poor Screech! His parents went out of town to an Elvis convention, and things got out of hand at their house. We had a lot of people over to the house, and someone accidently knocked over Screech's mother's favorite Elvis statue—oops! I had this idea to hold a poker game to try to win some money to buy a new statue. But the idea backfired, and Maxwell Nerdstrom ended up winning Screech's hound dog in the game—oops again! Amazingly enough, everything worked out okay. Maxwell traded the dog for a date with Jessie, and I came up with another idea, which worked this time. We had a party and charged admission. All the money we collected went to pay for a new statue.

Right after I asked Kelly to go steady, I met the new school nurse, Jennifer. Boy was she CUTE! Here I am imagining myself as a doctor and Kelly and Jennifer as my private nurses.

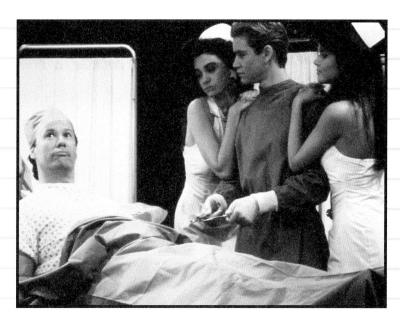

Not only did I have two beautiful nurses at my side, but I also got to "operate" on Mr. Belding!

Here's Screech, Slater, and I playing badminton. We had so much fun in the park that day! Lisa had her camera with her and took these shots.

This is one she took of me trying to look very macho, yet serious.

Screech is also trying to look serious in this shot. But how can you take someone who's wearing a fish shirt seriously?

This was taken on one of the best vacations I ever had! Jessie, Slater, Lisa, Kelly, Screech, and I were all invited to Kelly's grandfather's hotel, the Hawaiian Hideaway. The hotel was a little on the rustic side, but we still had the most amazing time of our lives!

From the time the plane left the airport in California until the time we landed in Hawaii, Jessie and Slater argued. Lisa made a bet with them that they wouldn't be able to stop arguing for the whole two weeks in Hawaii. Believe me, they couldn't wait to get back home so they could start all over again! This picture was taken during a brief intermission from arguing!

Looking good!

Screech was mistaken for a lost chief from a native Hawaiian tribe. What a laugh!

All right now ... everyone smile and say "pineapple!"

Kelly and Lisa were really into learning how to hula dance. Here they are in the middle of a hula lesson.

Don't they look like they were born to hula?

I met this amazing girl, Andrea, in Hawaii. Her daughter, Jennifer, was really great, too. It was so hard saying goodbye to both of them when we had to go back home.

Aloha!

Jessie took this goofy picture of me and Slater pounding out some not-so-Hawaiian sounds on the drums.

Forever Friends!

Just one of the many times I tried to reason with my good buddy, Screech.

Friends make the holidays so much fun!

Here we are hanging around in the school cafeteria. Even if the food stinks, the company's always good.

Slater and I were off to catch **some** waves together.

Jessie, Lisa, and Kelly were all ready to have some fun in the sun, too!

Look, it's a photo of the entire gang, including Mr. Belding. What a rare moment in history — having everyone together for a picture!

The gang's all here! Thanks to these guys, my high school years have been a blast.

Here are some fun photos of me and the gang ... and that wraps up my scrapbook!